Amazons & Warriors
Adult Coloring Book

VOLUME 1

AUSXIP Coloring Books

AUSXIP Publishing - Sydney, Australia
www.ausxippublishing.com

Cover design by Mary D. Brooks
Illustrations Copyright © 2015 by AUSXIP Publishing
Book design and production by AUSXIP Publishing

ISBN-10:0-9944765-0-7
ISBN-13:978-0-9944765-0-0

Printed in the United States

WHY SHOULD WE COLOR?

How does coloring help? Isn't that just for children? Psychologist Gloria Martinez Ayala recently discussed why it's so important for adults as well as children. She was interviewed by the Huffington Post where she said: "The relaxation that it provides lowers the activity of the amygdala, a basic part of our brain involved in controlling emotion that is affected by stress."

So what does that mean? It means by immersing ourselves in one activity that our energies are totally focused, our brains are not focused on the things that stress us out. This is quite true. It does work.

Break out your favorite coloring pencils/crayons / paints - however you want to do it, do it!

HOW TO USE THIS BOOK

1. It's time to set aside time for yourself. Alert your family and friends, shut the door, turn off the tv, the internet and your cell phone. It's YOUR time.

2. Break out the crayons, the pencils or the markers. Each design has it's own page and no design behind the page the illustration is on that will affect the design behind it. You can use pencils, crayons or markers. It's your choice how you draw, what colors to use - there is absolutely no wrong or right way to do this. Don't think about it, just color!

If you don't finish in one sitting, that's okay. Come back to it. It's your time and your choice how quickly or slowly you color. Remember...it's FUN.

IMPORTANT: Find a place where it's quiet, turn off the tv, the cell phone, the noise. The whole point of coloring in is to help you to relax. The only way you will do that is if you are not distracted.

Color away and just relax. The world will still be there once you are ready to put aside your coloring book and you will be less stressed. You can come back to it any time.

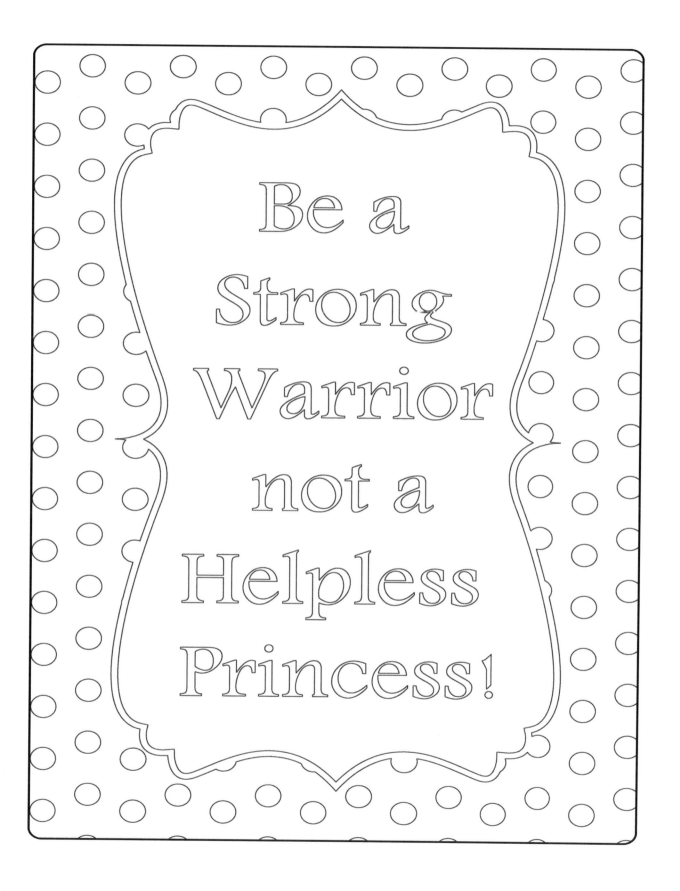

JOAN OF ARC - 1412 to 1431

"I am not afraid... I was born to do this."

AMELIA EARHART 1897 - 1937

"I want to do is because I want to do it. Women must try to do things as men have tried. When they fail, their failure must be but a challenge to others."

Sign Up For: TO COLORING TO RELAX Newsletter

Our newsletter is sent out with the latest news about upcoming releases and a free design for you to color each month. Sign up now!

Go here to sign up!

http://eepurl.com/bCDwe1

Other Boosk Published by AUSXIP Publishing

Coloring To Relax The Mind - Adult Coloring Books

Available in Print and PDF

1. Volume 1 - 50 Designs - Mandalas and Geometric Designs
2. Volume 2 - 30 Designs - Under The Sea
3. Volume 3 - 30 Designs - Winter Wonderland